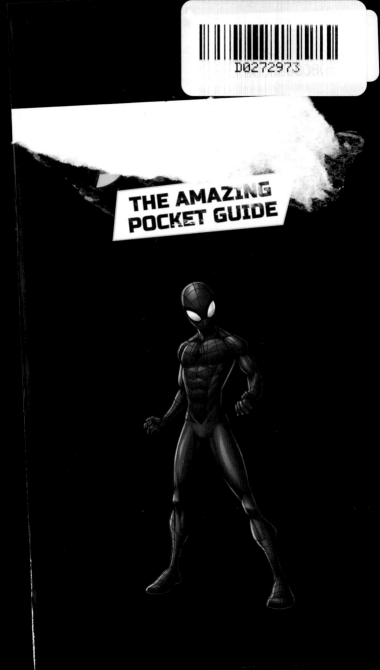

THE AMAZING POCKET GUIDE

Senior Editor David Fentiman
Senior Art Editor Nathan Martin, David McDonald
Senior Production Editor Jennifer Murray
Senior Production Controller Mary Slater
Managing Editor Emma Grange
Managing Art Editor Vicky Short
Publishing Director Mark Searle

Designed for DK by Lisa Sodeau; written by Catherine Saunders

This edition first published in Great Britain in 2023 by
Dorling Kindersley Limited
DK, One Embassy Gardens, 8 Viaduct Gardens,
London SW11 7BW

Contains content previously published in *Marvel Spider-Man Pocket Expert* (2022)

The authorised representative in the EEA is
Dorling Kindersley Verlag GmbH. Arnulfstr. 124,
80636 Munich, Germany

Page design copyright © 2023 Dorling Kindersley Limited
A Penguin Random House Company

© 2023 MARVEL

10 9 8 7 6 5 4 3 2 1
001–335605–Feb/2023

A CIP catalogue record for this book is available
from the British Library.
ISBN 978-0-2416-1924-7

Printed and bound in China

For the curious

www.dk.com
www.marvel.com

MIX
Paper | Supporting
responsible forestry
FSC™ C018179

This book was made with Forest
Stewardship Council ™ certified
paper – one small step in DK's
commitment to a sustainable future.
**For more information go to
www.dk.com/our-green-pledge**

MARVEL
SPIDER-MAN

THE AMAZING POCKET GUIDE

This book belongs to

_____

I am a reader and I celebrated World Book Day 2023
with this gift from my local bookseller and
Dorling Kindersley Limited.

WORLD BOOK DAY®

World Book Day's mission is to offer every child and
young person the opportunity to read and love books
by giving you the chance to have a book of your own.

To find out more, and for fun activities including the
monthly World Book Day Book Club, video stories and
book recommendations, visit **worldbookday.com**

World Book Day is a charity
sponsored by National Book Tokens.

PETER PARKER

Peter Parker was a high school student who loved science and hated sports. A bite from a radioactive spider changed his life overnight. It gave him amazing powers. And with that came great responsibilities...

⚡ RATING

FIGHTING SKILLS
●●●●●●○

SPEED
●●●●●●○

STRENGTH
●●●●●●○

KEY ABILITIES

- ☑ Science
- ☑ Inventing
- ☑ Teaching
- ☑ Photography
- ☑ Keeping secrets

SECRET IDENTITY

Peter knew that it would put his family at risk if he told them about his powers. So he kept them secret from everyone.

SPIDER-MAN

At first, Peter used his powers to find fame as a wrestler, but he soon realized that was not who he wanted to be. Now, whenever his spider-sense tells him that someone is in trouble, he'll do whatever he can to help.

⚡ RATING

FIGHTING SKILLS
●●●●●●●○○○

SPEED
●●●●●●●●○○

STRENGTH
●●●●●●●○○○

WEB-SLINGER

Spidey uses his web-shooters to swing above the city. His feet and hands can also stick to most surfaces, which makes wall-crawling easy, too.

KEY ABILITIES

Name: Peter Parker

- ☑ Agility
- ☑ Reflexes
- ☑ Healing power
- ☑ Spider-sense warns of danger

MILES MORALES

⚡ RATING

FIGHTING SKILLS
●●●●●●●○○○

SPEED
●●●●●●●○○○

STRENGTH
●●●●●●●○○○

Teenager Miles Morales was just trying to adjust to a new school and make friends when a spider bite changed his life. Sound familiar? Miles has a lot to learn, but at least he has Peter Parker (and several other spider-heroes) who understand exactly how he feels.

OUCH!

The spider that bites Miles had hitched a ride with Miles' uncle Aaron, aka the Prowler.

KEY ABILITIES

☑ Science
☑ Maths
☑ Graffiti art
☑ Sense of humour
☑ Facing up to problems

SPIDER-MAN

Miles Morales has all of Peter's amazing powers, plus two useful extras of his own – spider-camouflage and "venom blasts". With his spider-camouflage, Miles can be almost invisible and he can also temporarily paralyse foes with his venom blasts.

⚡ RATING

FIGHTING SKILLS
●●●●●●○

SPEED
●●●●○○●

STRENGTH
●●●●○●●

KEY ABILITIES

Name: Miles Morales

☑ Spider-camouflage
☑ Venom blasts
☑ Agility
☑ Healing power
☑ Spider-sense

BEING HIMSELF

There are many different spider-heroes in many different universes, but Miles is working out exactly what kind of Spider-Man he wants to be.

AARON DAVIS

⚡ RATING

FIGHTING SKILLS
●●●●●●○○

SPEED
●●●●●○○○

STRENGTH
●●●●○○○○

Aaron Davis might be a criminal with some very bad friends, but he is also Miles Morales' uncle. He loves his nephew and offers him advice and encouragement when he needs it.

FAMILY ISSUES

When the Prowler and Spider-Man clash, neither one knows whom they're really fighting.

🧠 KEY ABILITIES

Alias: the Prowler

☑ Master thief
☑ Athlete
☑ Expert acrobat
☑ Expert martial artist

AUNT MAY PARKER

When Peter Parker's parents go missing, presumed dead, his aunt and uncle welcome him into their home. After Uncle Ben is killed by a burglar, Aunt May raises Peter alone.

⚡ RATING

FIGHTING SKILLS
●●●●●●○

SPEED
●●●●●●○

STRENGTH
●●●●●●○

GETTING MARRIED

After Ben's death, May finds love with Jay Jameson, father of J Jonah Jameson. Unlike his son, Jay is a big fan of Spidey.

KEY TRAITS

Name: Maybelle Parker

- ☑ Practical
- ☑ Responsible
- ☑ Caring
- ☑ Resourceful
- ☑ Supportive

BLACK CAT

RATING

FIGHTING SKILLS
●●●●●●●○

SPEED
●●●●●●●○

STRENGTH
●●●●●●●○

Black Cat is a reformed (mostly) burglar. Like a cat, she is stealthy, agile, and cunning – skills that made her a successful burglar, but also a great asset to any Super Hero team.

FRIEND OR FOE?

Spidey has been a good influence on Black Cat, but sometimes the two friends still fight on different sides.

KEY ABILITIES

Name: Felicia Hardy

☑ Athlete

☑ Martial artist

☑ Safecracking/lock picking

☑ Manipulating her surroundings to bring bad luck on others

BLACK PANTHER

T'Challa is not just the king of Wakanda, he is also his country's warrior champion, Black Panther. He wears a special Vibranium suit which absorbs impact and protects him from injury.

⚡ RATING

FIGHTING SKILLS
●●●●●●●○

SPEED
●●●●●●●○

STRENGTH
●●●●○●●○

KEY ABILITIES

Name: T'Challa

- ☑ Genius-level intelligence
- ☑ Tactics and strategy
- ☑ Enhanced senses
- ☑ Tracking
- ☑ Healing

LEADER

Black Panther has worked with Spidey as part of the Avengers. Black Panther led the team for a while.

HERO

BLACK WIDOW

⚡ RATING

FIGHTING SKILLS
●●●●●●●○○○

SPEED
●●●●●●●○○○

STRENGTH
●●●●●●○○○○

Black Widow is a former Russian spy who often works with Spider-Man as part of the Avengers. She's tough, brave, and extremely agile, and also uses her spy skills to assist SHIELD when needed.

TEACHER

Black Widow also helps to train Miles Morales and his Champions teammates.

KEY ABILITIES

Name: Natalia Romanova/
Natasha Romanoff

☑ Enhanced speed and strength

☑ Weapons expert

☑ Gymnast

CAPTAIN AMERICA

Captain America understands better than most how Peter felt when he became Spider-Man. Cap's own body was transformed by Super-Soldier Serum and his life changed dramatically.

⚡ RATING

FIGHTING SKILLS
●●●●●●●○

SPEED
●●●●●●●○

STRENGTH
●●●●○●●○

BEHIND THE SUIT

Sometimes, Cap likes to ride his motorcycle and try to remember what it feels like to be an ordinary person.

KEY ABILITIES

Name: Steve Rogers

- ☑ Enhanced human physique
- ☑ Master of martial arts
- ☑ Skilled acrobat
- ☑ Master tactician

CAPTAIN MARVEL

Former US Air Force pilot, astronaut, and intelligence agent, Carol Danvers was a pretty impressive person even before an accident turned her into a human-Kree hybrid with super-powers.

⚡ RATING

FIGHTING SKILLS
●●●●●●●○○

SPEED
●●●●●●○○○

STRENGTH
●●●●●●●○○

TEAM PLAYER

Captain Marvel and Spidey have been friends for years and often team up in the New Avengers.

KEY ABILITIES

Name: Carol Danvers

☑ Flight, even in space

☑ Healing

☑ Durability

☑ Control, absorb, and discharge energy

CARNAGE

When part of the alien symbiote Venom attached itself to vicious criminal Cletus Kasady, the result was a powerful and relentless Super Villain. Worse still, it absolutely hates Spider-Man.

⚡ RATING

FIGHTING SKILLS
●●●●●●●○

SPEED
●●●●●●○○

STRENGTH
●●●●●●○○

KEY ABILITIES

Name: Cletus Kasady

- ☑ No regard for human life
- ☑ Enormous strength
- ☑ Create sharp weapons or long tentacles with its body

DEADLY ENEMY

It's hard to know who Carnage hates more, Spidey or Venom. In any case, it is stronger than both of them combined.

VILLAIN

CHAMELEON

One of Spider-Man's oldest foes, Chameleon can copy anyone's appearance. His career as a spy was thwarted by Spidey, so he became a master criminal instead. Naturally, he now hates Spider-Man.

⚡ RATING

FIGHTING SKILLS
●●●●●●●○

SPEED
●●●●●●●○

STRENGTH
●●●●●●●○

KEY ABILITIES

Name: Dmitri Smerdyakov
- ☑ Disguise
- ☑ Mimicry
- ☑ Spying
- ☑ Increased lifespan

MASTERMIND

Chameleon can keep up his disguises for months at a time and he has impersonated Spidey many times.

DOCTOR DOOM

Doctor Doom combines the powers of science and sorcery. He's brilliant but bitter and determined to take over the world, starting with his home country of Latveria.

⚡ RATING

FIGHTING SKILLS
●●●●●●○○

SPEED
●●●●●●○○

STRENGTH
●●●●●○○○

KEY ABILITIES

Name: Victor von Doom

- ☑ Genius-level intelligence
- ☑ Magic
- ☑ Martial arts
- ☑ Weapons expert

WORTHY FOE

As Reed Richards' friend, Spidey is naturally Doctor Doom's enemy and part of his quest for revenge. It seems that Doom may have won this round...

DOCTOR OCTOPUS

⚡ RATING

FIGHTING SKILLS
●●●●●●○○

SPEED
●●●●●●○○

STRENGTH
●●●●●●○○

Doc Ock is an evil genius who controls four steel tentacles with his mind. He'll try anything to defeat Spider-Man, from creating an army of Octobots to romancing Peter's Aunt May!

NEW PLAN

Doc Ock has even tried becoming Spider-Man, but he's just not cut out to be a Super Hero.

🧠 KEY ABILITIES

Name: Dr Otto Octavius

☑ Scientific genius

☑ Agility

☑ Strategy and planning

☑ Super-strength

DOCTOR STRANGE

As Earth's Sorcerer Supreme, Doctor Strange is a master of magic. He's a great friend to Spidey and can instantly appear in spirit form whenever the web-slinger needs his advice.

⚡ RATING

FIGHTING SKILLS
●●●●●●○

SPEED
●●●●●●○

STRENGTH
●●●●●○○

IN PERSON

When Spidey needs back up, Doctor Strange can teleport right into the action to help.

KEY ABILITIES

Name: Dr Stephen Strange

- ☑ Magic
- ☑ Martial arts
- ☑ Energy manipulation
- ☑ Teleportation
- ☑ Controlling time

ELECTRO

⚡ RATING

FIGHTING SKILLS
●●●●●●●○○

SPEED
●●●●●●●○○

STRENGTH
●●●●●●●○○

An accident left Max Dillon with the power to generate and control electricity. He can black out a whole city in seconds, and he can recharge his powers from any electrical source.

SHOCKING!

Even Spidey has no defence against an electric shock, but he has still been able to defeat Electro in their many battles.

KEY ABILITIES

Name: Maxwell Dillon

☑ Generating electricity

☑ Projecting lightning bolts

☑ Travelling by "riding" on electricity

FLASH THOMPSON

Eugene "Flash" Thompson is a reformed school bully who is now one of Peter Parker's closest friends. He got super-powers from the symbiote Venom, but uses them for good. He is known as Agent Anti-Venom.

⚡ RATING

FIGHTING SKILLS
●●●●●●○○

SPEED
●●●●●○○○

STRENGTH
●●●●○○○○

CHANGING

Flash used to bully Peter, but he's changed. He served in the US Army and is one of Spidey's most loyal supporters.

KEY ABILITIES
Names:
Eugene "Flash" Thompson/
Agent Anti-Venom

☑ Super-human stamina
☑ Durability
☑ Some Spidey-like powers
☑ Healing

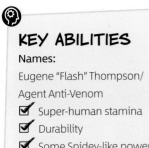

GANKE LEE

⚡ RATING

FIGHTING SKILLS
●●●●●●○

SPEED
●●●●●●○

STRENGTH
●●●●●●○

Ganke Lee is Miles Morales' school roommate and best friend. Ganke knows Miles' secret and helps his friend to work out how to balance being a Super Hero and a teenager.

🧠 KEY TRAITS

Alias: Ned (it's a long story)

- ☑ Smart
- ☑ Trustworthy
- ☑ Loyal
- ☑ Enthusiastic
- ☑ Good at keeping secrets (mostly)

🕸 WORKING IT OUT

Ganke helps Miles to understand his powers, and offers advice on what the rookie hero should do.

22

GHOST-SPIDER

Gwen Stacy is important to Spider-Man in many universes. However, in Earth-65 it is a teenage Gwen, not Peter Parker, who gains spider-like super-powers. She becomes Ghost-Spider, aka Spider-Woman.

⚡ RATING

FIGHTING SKILLS
●●●●●●○

SPEED
●●●●●○○

STRENGTH
●●●●●○○

TEENAGE LIFE

Gwen is friends with the non-super-powered Peter Parker in her universe. He is a big fan of Spider-Woman!

KEY ABILITIES

Name: Gwen Stacy

☑ Wall-crawling

☑ Super-human strength

☑ Super-human agility

☑ Spider-sense

23

GREEN GOBLIN

Businessman Norman Osborn became the Green Goblin after an experimental serum gave him super-strength. As Green Goblin, his quest for chaos and destruction has led to many battles with Spider-Man.

⚡ RATING

FIGHTING SKILLS
●●●●●●○

SPEED
●●●●●●○

STRENGTH
●●●●●●○

KEY ABILITIES

Name: Norman Osborn

- ☑ Super-human agility
- ☑ Super-human stamina
- ☑ Healing/regeneration
- ☑ Intelligence

FIRE POWER

Green Goblin fights Spidey with an explosive array of pumpkin bombs and gas grenades.

HARRY OSBORN

Harry is the son of Norman Osborn, aka the Green Goblin. Although he has been friends with Peter Parker since university, he cannot always be relied on to do the right thing. He's even taken over as Green Goblin several times.

⚡ RATING

FIGHTING SKILLS
●●●●●●●○○○

SPEED
●●●●●●●●○○

STRENGTH
●●●●●●●○○○

JUST LIKE DAD

Taking Goblin Serum gives Harry amazing powers, but it costs him his sanity. As the Green Goblin, Harry will do anything to defeat Spidey.

KEY ABILITIES

Names: Harold Osborn

☑ Genius-level intelligence

☑ Super-human strength

☑ Super-human stamina (all from Goblin Serum)

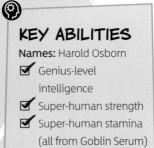

25

HOBGOBLIN

⚡ RATING

FIGHTING SKILLS
●●●●●●●○○○

SPEED
●●●●●●○○○○

STRENGTH
●●●○●○○○○○

Fashion designer Roderick Kingsley will do anything to achieve success. When he found Norman Osborn's Green Goblin Serum, he didn't hesitate in taking it. It turned him into the villainous Hobgoblin.

🧠 KEY ABILITIES

Name: Roderick Kingsley
- ☑ Durability
- ☑ Agility
- ☑ Healing
- ☑ Quick reflexes

GOBLIN GLIDER

Hobgoblin has the same equipment as the Green Goblin. The goblin glider gives him an advantage in this battle with Miles Morales.

HULK

An accident involving gamma radiation gave scientist Bruce Banner incredible powers. Now whenever he's angry he transforms into a massive green Super Hero, Hulk.

⚡ RATING

FIGHTING SKILLS
●●●●●●○○

SPEED
●●●●●●○○

STRENGTH
●●●●●●○○

KEY ABILITIES

Name: Bruce Banner

☑ Almost limitless strength

☑ Virtually indestructible

☑ Stamina and durability

☑ Genius-level intelligence

FRIEND OR FOE?

Hulk is an Avenger, but sometimes his unstable personality causes him to battle his friends (like Spidey) instead.

HYDRO-MAN

⚡ RATING

FIGHTING SKILLS
●●●●●●○

SPEED
●●●●●●○

STRENGTH
●●●●●●○

Ship's crewman Morris Bench gained super-powers when he fell overboard and came into contact with an experimental power generator. He can now transform into a liquid Super Villain known as Hydro-Man.

DOUBLE TROUBLE

When Hydro-Man teams up with Sandman, they create an even worse problem for Spidey – Mud-Thing. Yuck!

KEY ABILITIES

Name: Morris Bench

☑ Transform into a liquid

☑ Create water blasts

☑ Control water

☑ Travel through other liquids

IRON MAN

Billionaire businessman Tony Stark is an engineering genius. He invented the first Iron Man suit to save his life. He's worn the armour many times since then and is now a fully-fledged Super Hero.

⚡ RATING

FIGHTING SKILLS
●●●●●●○○

SPEED
●●●●●●●○

STRENGTH
●●●●●●○○

KEY ABILITIES

Name: Tony Stark

☑ Genius-level intelligence
☑ Super-strength (in armour)
☑ Durability (in armour)
☑ Magnetism (in armour)

MENTOR

Iron Man is a mentor to both Peter Parker and Miles Morales. They both work with him as part of the Avengers.

J JONAH JAMESON

One of Spider-Man's most dedicated foes is not even a Super Villain. Newspaper editor J Jonah Jameson thinks that Spidey is a public menace and is determined to ruin his reputation.

⚡ RATING

FIGHTING SKILLS
●●●●●●●○

SPEED
●●●●●●○○

STRENGTH
●●●●●●○○

BITTER FOE

Jameson distrusts all costumed Super Heroes. He doesn't believe heroes like Spidey are truly good.

KEY TRAITS

Name: John Jonah Jameson

☑ Hard working
☑ Tenacious
☑ Determined
☑ Stubborn

JACKAL

Miles Warren is a college science professor and cloning expert. However, his secret cloning experiments usually have disastrous results. One turned him into the villainous and unstable Jackal.

⚡ RATING

FIGHTING SKILLS
●●●●●●●○

SPEED
●●●●●●○○

STRENGTH
●●●●●●○○

KEY ABILITIES

Name: Miles Warren

☑ Genius-level intelligence
☑ Agility
☑ Super-human leaping
☑ Martial arts

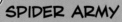

SPIDER ARMY

The Jackal developed a whole army of spider clones, but their arachnid powers did not work on Spidey.

31

JEFF MORALES

⚡ **RATING**

FIGHTING SKILLS
●●●●●●●○

SPEED
●●●●●●●○

STRENGTH
●●●●●●●○

Miles Morales' dad, Jeff, tries hard to be a good person and a great father. As a police officer, his job is to uphold the law. He's not a fan of Super Heroes like Spidey, who just swing in and grab all the glory.

NEW HERO

Miles is scared to tell his dad that he's Spidey. But Jeff sees something different in the new Spider-Man.

KEY TRAITS

Also known as:

Officer Morales

☑ Honest

☑ Determined

☑ Fair

☑ Brave

KINGPIN

Ruthless crime boss Wilson Fisk, aka Kingpin, will do anything to gain power. He doesn't care who he has to betray, swindle, or hurt – and somehow he's been elected mayor of New York City. Spider-Man has had many run-ins with this Super Villain.

⚡ RATING

FIGHTING SKILLS
●●●●●●●○

SPEED
●●●●●○●○

STRENGTH
●●●●●○○○

🧠 KEY ABILITIES

Name: Wilson Fisk

☑ Criminal mastermind
☑ Peak human strength
☑ Multilingual
☑ Enormous willpower

FREQUENT FOE

Even two powerful Super Heroes can't get the better of Kingpin. He has Spidey and Human Torch in the palm of his hand!

KRAVEN THE HUNTER

⚡ RATING

FIGHTING SKILLS
●●●●●●●○○

SPEED
●●●●●●●○○

STRENGTH
●●●●●●●○○

Magical powers make Kraven a fearsome predator. However, he won't rest until he is the best hunter that has ever lived. To achieve that, he's decided that he needs to defeat the ultimate foe – Spider-Man.

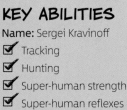

🧠 KEY ABILITIES

Name: Sergei Kravinoff
- ☑ Tracking
- ☑ Hunting
- ☑ Super-human strength
- ☑ Super-human reflexes

🕸 NEW KRAVEN

Ultimately, Sergei fails to complete his mission, so his daughter Ana takes over. She is just as determined to hunt down Spidey.

LIVING BRAIN

The Living Brain was billed as the most intelligent robot ever. It was said to know the answer to any question, including: Who is Spider-Man? However, it malfunctioned before it got a chance to reveal the secret.

⚡ RATING

FIGHTING SKILLS
●●●●●●●○○○

SPEED
●●●●●●○○○○

STRENGTH
●●●●●●○○○○

KEY ABILITIES

Also known as: Brain
- ☑ Self-repairing
- ☑ Super-human strength
- ☑ Super-human durability
- ☑ Artificial intelligence

ROBOT RAMPAGE

Two greedy crooks broke the Living Brain, but Spidey captured them and the renegade robot.

LIZARD

⚡ RATING

FIGHTING SKILLS
●●●●●●●○

SPEED
●●●●●●●○

STRENGTH
●●●●●●●○

Dr Curt Connors is a surgeon who lost his arm in a wartime bomb blast. By studying reptiles that can regenerate lost limbs, he created a secret formula that restored his arm. But it also turned him into the villain Lizard.

IT'S COMPLICATED

Dr Connors is friends with Spidey, but when he transforms into Lizard he has no memory of their friendship.

KEY ABILITIES

Name: Dr Curt Connors

☑ Clinging to walls
☑ Controlling other reptiles
☑ Regenerative healing
☑ Super reflexes

MARY JANE WATSON

Next-door-neighbour Mary Jane Watson is the love of Peter's life. Popular, funny, and confident, MJ is the opposite of shy and awkward Peter, but their different personalities complement each other and they are a great team.

⚡ RATING

FIGHTING SKILLS
●●●●●●○○

SPEED
●●●●●●○○

STRENGTH
●●●●●●○○

RELATIONSHIP

Being close to a Super Hero is not easy. Being Spidey takes up a lot of Peter's time and energy and often puts MJ in danger.

KEY ABILITIES

Also known as: MJ

☑ Acting
☑ Dancing
☑ Running a business
☑ Good at keeping secrets

MOLTEN MAN

⚡ RATING

FIGHTING SKILLS
●●●●●●○○○○

SPEED
●●●●●●●○○○

STRENGTH
●●●●●●○○○○

Molten Man was created when lab assistant Mark Raxton spilt a hot liquid metallic alloy on himself. It absorbed into his skin, turning it golden and giving him super-human abilities.

KEY ABILITIES

Name: Mark Raxton

☑ Super-human strength

☑ Needs little sleep

☑ Resistant to injury

☑ Creating fire

☑ His touch can melt or burn anything

HOT STUFF

Although he can be hot-tempered, Molten Man usually prefers helping Spidey to fighting him. But not always!

MS MARVEL

High-schooler and Super Hero fan Kamala Khan developed super-powers after being surrounded by the Terrigen Mists. The mutation-causing vapour gave her stretchy super-powers and she named herself in honour of her favourite hero, Captain Marvel.

⚡ RATING

FIGHTING SKILLS
●●●●●●○○

SPEED
●●●●●○○○

STRENGTH
●●●●●○○○

KEY ABILITIES

Name: Kamala Khan

☑ Stretching

☑ Shrinking

☑ Rapid healing

☑ Can alter appearance

FLEXIBLE HERO

Kamala's body can shrink, stretch, or expand to any shape. That's handy when teaming up with Spidey and the Champions.

VILLAIN

MYSTERIO

⚡ RATING

FIGHTING SKILLS
●●●●●●○○○○

SPEED
●●●●●●●○○○

STRENGTH
●●●●●●○○○○

Special effects expert and stunt man Quentin Beck wanted fame, so he turned to crime. He has no super-powers, so he uses tricks and illusions to fool people. But Mysterio is (generally) no match for Spidey.

STAGE PROPS

Mysterio tries to pretend he has magical powers, but it is just clever stage tricks, props, and special effects. These illusions are mostly useless against genuine Super Heroes like Spidey.

KEY ABILITIES

Name: Quentin Beck

☑ Visual effects and stunts

☑ Basic hypnotism

☑ Acting

☑ Mechanical engineering

☑ Meticulous planning

NICK FURY

ALLY

A veteran of the US Army, Nick Fury is highly trained in combat and an expert in stealth missions. Now an agent of the secretive SHIELD organization, Nick is dedicated to doing what he believes is right.

⚡ RATING

FIGHTING SKILLS
●●●●●●●○○

SPEED
●●●●●●○○○

STRENGTH
●●●●●●○○○

KEY ABILITIES

Also known as:

Nick Fury Jr/Marcus Johnson

☑ Combat expert

☑ Durability

☑ Weapons expert

☑ Peak human strength

TOUGH BUT FAIR

When Nick first meets the young Peter Parker, he is a tough mentor. He wants Peter to become a truly great Super Hero.

NOVA

RATING

FIGHTING SKILLS
●●●●●●●○○○

SPEED
●●●●●●●○○○

STRENGTH
●●●●●●●○○○

Sam Alexander doesn't believe his father's stories of his work in the Nova Corps, a team of space peacekeepers. However, when Sam puts on his dad's black helmet, he sees that it's all true. Now it's Sam's turn to be Nova.

TEEN TEAM

His newfound abilities makes teenage Sam a little arrogant. Ms Marvel finds him very annoying at first.

KEY ABILITIES

Name: Sam Alexander

☑ Intergalactic flight

☑ Super-human speed

☑ Durability

☑ Control Nova Force energy

PENI PARKER

Peni Parker was raised by her Aunt May and Uncle Ben after her father died. Does that all sound a bit familiar? Well, in an alternate universe this brave middle school student is her city's spider-suited protector.

⚡ RATING

FIGHTING SKILLS
●●●●●○○○

SPEED
●●●●●○○○

STRENGTH
●●●●●○○○

KEY ABILITIES

Alias: SP//dr

☑ Strength
☑ Durability
☑ Web-shooting
☑ Resistant to damage
   (all while in armour)

DOUBLE LIFE

When she's not battling Super Villains, Peni is just an average teenage vegetarian with too much homework!

RHINO

⚡ RATING

FIGHTING SKILLS
●●●●●●○○○

SPEED
●●●●●●○○○

STRENGTH
●●●●●●○○○

Aleksei Sytsevich was just a regular villain until he took part in a secret experiment, which bonded a tough, rhino-like armour to his body. Now known as Rhino, he's fast, super strong, and virtually unstoppable.

BRAINS VS BRAWN

Rhino might be super strong but he's certainly not super smart or even very agile. Clever Spidey can usually defeat him.

KEY ABILITIES

Name: Aleksei Sytsevich

☑ Super-human stamina
☑ Resistant to injury
☑ Can go days without sleep
☑ Charging at foes

RIO MORALES

Rio Morales believes in facing problems rather than avoiding them. She tells her son Miles that their family does not run from things. However, she has no idea about all the Spidey-related stuff that Miles is dealing with!

⚡ RATING

FIGHTING SKILLS
●●●●●●○

SPEED
●●●●●●○

STRENGTH
●●●●●●○

BIG SECRET

Rio has no idea that the new Spider-Man is Miles. She thinks he is just worried about being at a new school!

KEY TRAITS
- ☑ Kind
- ☑ Hardworking
- ☑ Patient
- ☑ Brave
- ☑ Positive

⚡ RATING

FIGHTING SKILLS
●●●●●●●○○○

SPEED
●●●●●●●○○○

STRENGTH
●●●●●●●○○○

Sandman is former criminal William Baker. During a prison break he was accidentally exposed to radiation and his body became living sand. Sandman can shape-shift into any form or size.

🧠 KEY ABILITIES

Also known as:

William Baker, Flint Marko

☑ Shape-shifting

☑ Never needs to eat or drink

☑ Does not age

☑ Can become hard or soft sand

🕸 WORKING IT OUT

At first, Sandman used his powers to commit more crimes. Spidey eventually persuaded him to switch sides.

SCARLET SPIDER

Scarlet Spider is the most successful of Miles Warren's (aka the Jackal) spider clones. He was created to torment Spider-Man, but the two eventually became allies. Well, they do have a lot in common...

⚡ RATING

FIGHTING SKILLS
●●●●●●●○○○

SPEED
●●●●●●○○○○

STRENGTH
●●●●●●○○○

SMALL DIFFERENCE

Scarlet Spider has all the same abilities as Peter Parker, but he has added impact webbing and stingers to his arsenal.

KEY ABILITIES

Name: Ben Reilly
- ☑ Spider-sense
- ☑ Super-strength
- ☑ Agility
- ☑ Healing

SCORPION

Scorpion is one of Spider-Man's oldest and most persistent enemies. He got his powers when he took part in an animal mutation experiment. It gave him the strength and agility of a human-sized scorpion.

⚡ RATING

FIGHTING SKILLS
●●●●●●○

SPEED
●●●●●●○

STRENGTH
●●●●●○○

🧠 KEY ABILITIES

Name:

MacDonald "Mac" Gargan

☑ Super-strength
☑ Durability
☑ Agility
☑ Wall-crawling

HARD TO BEAT

His tough battlesuit with its deadly tail, plus his strength and speed, make Scorpion a dangerous foe. Just ask Miles Morales!

SHOCKER

Shocker is a thief and safecracker who used his time in prison to develop some useful gadgets. His "vibro-shock" gauntlets blast air that has been vibrated at a high frequency.

⚡ RATING

FIGHTING SKILLS
●●●●●●○

SPEED
●●●●●●○

STRENGTH
●●●●●●○

KEY ABILITIES

Name: Herman Schultz

☑ Safecracker

☑ Engineer (self-taught)

☑ Vibro blasts

☑ Long-range punching (with gauntlets)

EXTRA SHOCKING

An outbreak of Spider-Virus caused Shocker to develop extra arms. It made it even easier for him to rob banks.

HERO

SILK

⚡ RATING

FIGHTING SKILLS
●●●●●●○○

SPEED
●●●●●●○○

STRENGTH
●●●●●●○○

The spider that bit Peter Parker also bit another student, Cindy Moon. She discovered her powers when she accidentally webbed up her parents. A mysterious person then hid her away for many years to train her and keep her safe.

WEB-SLINGERS

Cindy was kept hidden for more than 10 years. When she finally got out, she found Spider-Man and adopted the name Silk.

🧠 KEY ABILITIES

Name: Cindy Moon

☑ Wall-crawling
☑ Silk-sense
☑ Agility
☑ Super-strength and stamina
☑ Eidetic (photographic) memory

50

SPIDER-GIRL

In an alternate future, Spider-Man's teenage daughter is a Super Hero. She faces a host of villains, including the Green Goblin's grandson, whilst also trying not to be late for school.

⚡ RATING

FIGHTING SKILLS
●●●●●●●○○

SPEED
●●●●●●●○○

STRENGTH
●●●●●●○○○

KEY ABILITIES

Name: May "Mayday" Parker

☑ Enhanced spider-sense
☑ Wall-crawling
☑ Agility
☑ Basketball

FAMILY TREE

Mary Jane is May's mum. May inherited her red hair and outgoing personality, and her dad's spider-like super-powers.

51

SPIDER-HAM

⚡ RATING

FIGHTING SKILLS
●●●●●●○

SPEED
●●●●●●○

STRENGTH
●●●●●●○

In another universe, a spider was bitten by the pig May Porker after one of May's inventions went wrong. The bite turned the spider into a pig with spider abilities – aka Spider-Ham!

SWINE-ING INTO ACTION

Spider-Ham defeats villains such as Ducktor Doom with some Super Hero friends – Captain Americat, Hulk-Bunny, Iron Mouse, and the Fantastic Fur.

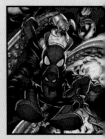

KEY ABILITIES

Name: Peter Porker

- ☑ Spider-sense
- ☑ Agility
- ☑ Healing
- ☑ Durability

SPIDER-MAN 2099

In one possible future universe, a lab accident gives scientist Miguel O'Hara similar powers to Spider-Man. However, he also has fangs, sharp claws, and can move so fast that he seems to leave a copy of himself behind!

⚡ RATING

FIGHTING SKILLS
●●●●●●○○

SPEED
●●●●●●○○

STRENGTH
●●●●●○○○

FAMILIAR FOE

Many of Spidey's old foes appear in Miguel's universe, too. He got the better of Scorpion by avoiding him!

KEY ABILITIES

Name: Miguel O'Hara

☑ Super-strength
☑ Agility
☑ Healing
☑ Telepathy

53

SPIDER-MAN NOIR

⚡ RATING

FIGHTING SKILLS
●●●●●○○○

SPEED
●●●●●●○○

STRENGTH
●●●●●●○○

In an alternate universe, it's still the 1930s, a time known as the Great Depression. This Peter Parker lives his life in black and white. When a spider bite gives him super-powers, he is determined to help as many people as possible.

KEY ABILITIES

Name: Peter Parker

☑ Wall-crawling
☑ Web-slinging
☑ Agility
☑ Stamina

NOT ALONE

There are many different Spider-people in alternate universes. Spider-Man Noir meets one with six arms!

SPIDER-WOMAN

Several heroes have taken on the name Spider-Woman, but Jessica Drew was the first. She got her powers when her scientist father gave her a special serum made from rare spiders to heal her when she was sick.

⚡ RATING

FIGHTING SKILLS
●●●●●●○○

SPEED
●●●●●●○○

STRENGTH
●●●●●○○○

KEY ABILITIES

Name: Jessica Drew

☑ Wall-crawling
☑ Agility
☑ Healing
☑ Super-human hearing

BEING A HERO

Jessica has worked with Spidey in the Avengers. Once, she was secretly replaced by a Skrull for a while. The other Avengers noticed, eventually...

STARLING

⚡ RATING

FIGHTING SKILLS
●●●●●●○

SPEED
●●●●●●○

STRENGTH
●●●●●●○

Tiana Toomes is the granddaughter of the Super Villain Vulture. Although her grandfather designed her suit and taught her how to use it, Tiana follows her own path and is more likely to help Spidey than battle him.

UNMASKING

Tiana meets Miles Morales when they're tracking the same villain. The teen heroes become friends and reveal their true identities.

🧠 KEY ABILITIES

Name: Tiana Toomes
- ☑ Flight (in harness)
- ☑ Super-strength (in harness)
- ☑ Tracking
- ☑ Artist

TERESA PARKER

Teresa Parker is Peter Parker's long-lost, secret sister. Their parents kept her birth secret, and when they died, she was adopted. For years, Teresa has no idea about her true identity and Peter does not know that she exists.

⚡ RATING

FIGHTING SKILLS
●●●●●●○○

SPEED
●●●●●●○○

STRENGTH
●●●●●●○○

BROTHER AND SISTER

Teresa first met Peter when she saved his life. The siblings are slowly getting to know each other.

🧠 KEY ABILITIES

Name:

Teresa Elizabeth Parker

☑ Spycraft

☑ Flight (in costume)

☑ Driving and piloting

☑ Improvisation

THOR

⚡ RATING

FIGHTING SKILLS
●●●●●●○○

SPEED
●●●●●●○○

STRENGTH
●●●●●●○○

Super Heroes don't come much mightier than Thor. Raised in Asgard, the home of the Norse gods, he's the God of Thunder. Thor was sent to Earth by his father Odin, and he helped to form the Avengers.

KEY ABILITIES

Name: Thor Odinson

☑ Durability
☑ Super-human senses
☑ Strength
☑ Nearly invulnerable

MAGICAL HAMMER

Thor's hammer, Mjolnir, enables him to fly. He can also use it to control lightning. Thor is normally the only one who can use Mjolnir.

TINKERER

Phineas Mason is a brilliant engineer and inventor who hates Super Heroes. He thinks that they use their powers too recklessly. As the Super Villain Tinkerer, he uses his skills to make weapons and gadgets to stop them.

⚡ RATING

FIGHTING SKILLS
●●●●●●○

SPEED
●●●●●●○

STRENGTH
●●●●●●○

ROBOT SUIT

Mason designed a special robot suit to trick Super Heroes and then attack them. Spider-Man was able to stop him.

KEY ABILITIES

Name: Phineas Mason
- ☑ Scientific genius
- ☑ Inventing
- ☑ Clever businessman
- ☑ Making weapons out of ordinary household objects

VENOM

⚡ RATING

FIGHTING SKILLS
●●●●●●○○

SPEED
●●●●●●●○

STRENGTH
●●●●●●○○

Venom is an alien symbiote, a parasite that survives by attaching itself to another creature. Venom has had various hosts, but it keeps returning to Eddie Brock, a journalist with a grudge against Spider-Man.

🧠 KEY ABILITIES

Name: Eddie Brock

☑ Shape-shifting
☑ Absorbing powers from host
☑ Camouflage
☑ Stamina

SPIDERS VS VENOM

Venom might have spider-like powers, but he's no match for the combined might of Peter Parker, Miles Morales, and Ghost-Spider.

VULTURE

Adrian Toomes was a late developer when it came to crime. After retiring from his job as an electrical engineer and inventor, he decided to use one of his creations to become a costumed criminal, Vulture.

⚡ RATING

FIGHTING SKILLS
●●●●●●●○○○

SPEED
●●●●●●●○○○

STRENGTH
●●●●●●○○○○

KEY ABILITIES

Name: Adrian Toomes
☑ Intelligence
☑ Invention
☑ Flight (in harness)
☑ Super-strength
   (in harness)

MATCH UP

Spidey has more super-powers than Vulture, but occasionally the older villain can outsmart him.

Happy
World Book Day!

When you've read this book, you can keep the fun going by: swapping it, talking about it with a friend, or reading it again!

What do you want to read next? Whether it's **comics**, **audiobooks recipe books** or **non-fiction**, you can visit your school, local library or nearest bookshop for your next read – someone will always be happy to help.

SPONSORED BY

Changing lives through a love of books and reading
World Book Day® is a charity sponsored by National Book Tokens

Illustration Allen Fatimaharan

World Book Day is about changing lives through reading

WORLD BOOK DAY
2 MARCH 2023

When children **choose to read** in their spare time it makes them

| Feel happier | Better at reading | More successful |

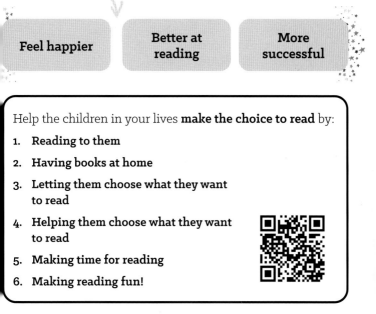

Help the children in your lives **make the choice to read** by:

1. **Reading to them**
2. **Having books at home**
3. **Letting them choose what they want to read**
4. **Helping them choose what they want to read**
5. **Making time for reading**
6. **Making reading fun!**

SPONSORED BY

NATIONAL BOOK tokens

Changing lives through a love of books and reading

World Book Day® is a charity sponsored by National Book Tokens

Illustration Allen Fatimaharan

IT'S SUPER HERO TIME!

What makes a **true Super Hero?** Find out in the **ultimate illustrated Spidey book**

Meet the World's **Mightiest Super Hero Team: The Avengers!** Discover their powers, allies, foes, and more

All about **Spidey** and his **friends,** with original Marvel images and awesome facts

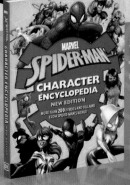

DK
MARVEL
© 2023 Marvel
dk.com